The *Roger Jones* Christmas Collection

Foreword by Chris Bowater

To Tim and Emma: *a Son and*
Daughter-in-law of whom
I am very proud

**kevin
mayhew**

kevin mayhew

First published in Great Britain in 2001 by Kevin Mayhew Ltd
Buxhall, Stowmarket, Suffolk IP14 3BW
Tel: +44 (0) 1449 737978 Fax: +44 (0) 1449 737834
E-mail: info@kevinmayhewltd.com

www.kevinmayhew.com

9 8 7 6 5 4 3 2 OD

ISBN 978 1 84003 745 6
ISMN M 57004 879 3
Catalogue No. 1450217

Cover design: Jonathan Stroulger
Music setting: Donald Thomson
Proof reading: Kate Gallaher

Printed and bound in Great Britain by CPI Antony Rowe Eastbourne

Important Copyright Information

The Publishers wish to express their gratitude to the copyright owners who have granted permission to include their copyright material in this book. Full details are indicated on the respective pages.

We would like to remind users of this hymnal that the reproduction of any hymn texts or music without the permission of the copyright holder is illegal. Details of all copyright holders are clearly indicated.

Most of the song texts and music are covered by a Christian Copyright Licensing (CCL) licence and a Music Reproduction Licence. If you possess a licence, it is essential that you check your instruction manual to ensure that the song you wish to use is covered.

If you are not a member of CCL, or the song you wish to reproduce is not covered by your licence, you must contact the copyright holder direct for their permission.

The reproduction of any music not covered by your licence is both illegal and immoral.

If you are interested in joining CCL they can be contacted at the following address: Christian Copyright Licensing (Europe) Ltd, PO Box 1339, Eastbourne, East Sussex BN 21 1AD. Tel: 01323 417711, www.ccli.co.uk

Contents

Roger Jones is Britain's foremost composer of Christian musicals and cantatas. Roger began writing musicals while teaching music in an inner-city comprehensive school in Birmingham in the early 1970s; his aim was to involve as many pupils and staff as possible in singing about and understanding biblical stories. Now, churches all over the world perform Roger's musicals, which are easily adaptable, whatever the resources available locally. This Christmas collection includes Roger's settings of many well-known and much-loved traditional carols, as well as new songs for Advent and Christmas, many of them from his four nativity musicals.

Annie Routley, the arranger and editor of many of these carols, has worked alongside Roger Jones at Christian Music Ministries since September 1994. A music graduate with a wide experience in playing viola and keyboards, and singing in choirs, small groups and broadcasts, Annie has in recent years with CMM been developing skills in orchestration and writing arrangements for groups in order to encourage musicians with a range of abilities.

CD and cassette recordings of *The Roger Jones Christmas Collection* are available from Christian Music Ministries, as are backing tracks on CD and cassette:

Christian Music Ministries, 325 Bromford Road, Hodge Hill, Birmingham, B36 8ET. Tel: 0121 783 3291 Fax: 0121 785 0500
www.cmm.org.uk

Foreword

I have known Roger for longer than either of us would really like to admit and had the honour of being a soloist on his very first musical project *Jerusalem Joy*. The rest, as they say, is history.

Roger's music has become established repertoire right across the spectrum of the church, here and overseas. His music has served as a bridge between traditional roots and the growing renewal churches for well over twenty years. This new collection will abundantly serve the insatiable appetite of the church for Christmas music. I am honoured to endorse the work of a friend and a contemporary musical craftsman.

CHRIS BOWATER

Note about using the backing tracks

The great advantage of singing to backing tracks is that they provide accompaniment and instruments that may not be available in the local situation. Singers also find it a great thrill to be accompanied by a larger instrumental ensemble.

Using backing tracks does not do away with the need to rehearse. Leaders, vocalists or choirs should become very familiar with speed, introductions, modulations, instrumental links and codas before using the tracks in worship. There must also be adequate sound reproduction equipment, appropriate to the size and acoustics of the room.

1 All my heart this night rejoices

Words: Paulus Gerhardt (1607-1676) and Catherine Winkworth (1827-1878)
Music: Roger Jones arr. Annie Routley. From *While Shepherds Watched* (1987)

STONEHOUSE 8 12 8 12

Moderato (♩ = 96)

1. All my heart this night re-joi-ces, as I hear, far and near, sweet-est an-gel voi-ces: 'Christ is born!' their choirs are sing-ing till the air ev-'ry-where now with joy is ring-ing!

Optional harmony for verse 3 (unaccompanied)

3. Come, then, let us has-ten yon-der, here let all, great and small,
kneel in awe and won-der; love him who with love is yearn-ing;

hail the star that from far bright with hope is burn - ing.

2. Hark, a voice from yonder manger,
   soft and sweet, does entreat: 'Flee from woe and danger
   each one come from all that grieves you
   you are freed; all you need I will surely give you!'

3. Come, then, let us hasten yonder,
   here let all, great and small, kneel in awe and wonder;
   love him who with love is yearning;
   hail the star that from far bright with hope is burning.

4. You, my Lord, I'll always cherish;
   live for you, and with you, dying, shall not perish;
   but shall dwell with you for ever
   far on high, in the joy that can alter never!

2 As with gladness men of old

Words: William Chatterton Dix (1837-1898)
Music: Roger Jones. From *Stargazers* (1976)

STARGAZERS 77 77 77

($\quad$ = 120)

1. As with glad-ness men of old did the guid-ing star be-hold, as with joy they hailed its light, lead-ing on-ward, beam-ing bright; so, most gra-cious Lord, may we e - ver-more be led to thee.

Optional choral 'Amen' ending

2. As with joyful steps they sped,
   to that lowly manger-bed,
   there to bend the knee before
   him whom heav'n and earth adore,
   so may we with willing feet
   ever seek thy mercy-scat.

3. As they offered gifts most rare
   at that manger rude and bare,
   so may we with holy joy,
   pure and free from sin's alloy,
   all our costliest treasures bring,
   Christ, to thee our heav'nly King.

4. Holy Jesus, ev'ry day
   keep us in the narrow way;
   and when earthly things are past,
   save our ransomed souls at last
   where they need no star to guide,
   where no clouds thy glory hide.

5. In the heav'nly country bright
   need they no created light,
   thou its light, its joy, its crown,
   thou its sun which goes not down;
   there for ever may we sing
   alleluias to our King.

3 Away in a manger

Words: William James Kirkpatrick (1838-1921), alt.
Music: Roger Jones. From *Away in a Manger* (1989)

BROMFORD 11 11 11 11

looked down   where he lay,

the lit - tle Lord Je - sus   a - sleep   on   the

hay.

2. The cattle are lowing, the baby awakes
   but little Lord Jesus, no crying he makes.
   I love you, Lord Jesus! Look down from on high
   and stay by my side until morning is nigh.

3. Be near me, Lord Jesus; I ask you to stay
   close by me for ever and love me, I pray.
   Bless all the dear children in your tender care,
   and fit us for heaven, to live with you there.

4 Benedictus
(Song of Zechariah)

Words and Music: Roger Jones arr. Annie Routley
From *Snakes and Ladders* (1999)

ZECHARIAH 9 11 11 9 and Refrain

Gently, with majesty ($\bullet$ = 120)

1. Praise to the Lord, the God of Is - ra - el, for he has come and has re-deemed his peo - ple. And raised up a horn of sal - va - tion for us in the house of his ser - vant Da - vid. Be -

2. Just as he promised his prophets long ago
   that we would be delivered from our enemies.
   He now has remembered his holy covenant
   that was made to our father Abraham.

5 Bethlehem

Words and Music: Roger Jones arr. Annie Routley
From *While shepherds watched* (1987)

MICAH 99 88

Andante con moto (♩ = 72)

2. Though we be like abandoned people,
   left alone all around is evil;
   then good news shall come to earth
   at the time that she gives birth!

3. He shall lead us just like a shepherd
   in his care and secure for ever;
   our great nation will never cease
   for he will become our peace!

6 Come, see the beauty of the King

Words and Music: Roger Jones arr. Annie Routley
From *While Shepherds Watched* (1987)

VENI VIDI 88 88 6

2. We see the beauty of the King,
   we see the Lord of ev'rything.
   His gentle hands, his lovely face,
   our praises bring, with angels sing!
   We come and worship him.

3. We see your beauty, you are King,
   we see you Lord of ev'rything.
   Your gentle hands, your lovely face,
   our praises bring, with angels sing!
   We come and worship you.

Optional harmony for verse 2

2. We see the beau - ty of the King, we see the Lord of ev - 'ry - thing. His gen - tle hands, his love - ly face!

Our prai - ses bring, with an - gels sing!

E⁷/G♯ A⁷/G D/F♯ E⁷/G♯

We come and wor - ship him.

D/A G/A Asus⁴ A⁷ D

D.C.

Optional descant for verse 3

3. Je - sus, you are King! You are the

D.C.

liv-ing God! We love you! We praise you! We wor-ship you!

7 Could it possibly happen to me?

Words and Music: Roger Jones arr. Annie Routley
From *While Shepherds Watched* (1987)

STECHFORD 12 9 12 9 and Refrain
Andante ritmico

1. What I saw in the sky from the
2. Was it true, what I heard when they
*3. Did the an - gels come near with the
4. Now I know what to do, for it

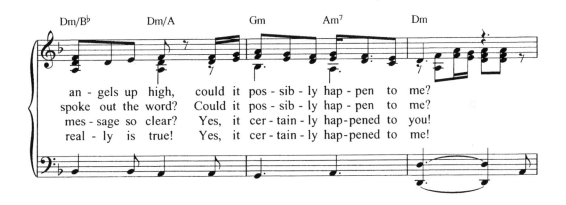

an - gels up high, could it pos - sib - ly hap - pen to me?
spoke out the word? Could it pos - sib - ly hap - pen to me?
mes - sage so clear? Yes, it cer - tain - ly hap-pened to you!
real - ly is true! Yes, it cer - tain - ly hap-pened to me!

Was it quite what it seemed, was it
That the child born this day is the
But I feel so con - fused! I just
So we'll go and we'll find he who's

Men and women sing alternate lines of verse 3, with the men singing the first line.

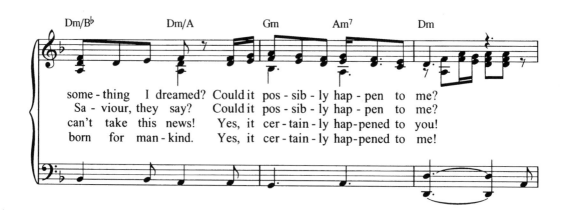

some - thing I dreamed? Could it pos - sib - ly hap - pen to me?
Sa - viour, they say? Could it pos - sib - ly hap - pen to me?
can't take this news! Yes, it cer - tain - ly hap-pened to you!
born for man - kind. Yes, it cer - tain - ly hap-pened to me!

Chorus

When I con - si - der the work of your fin - gers, the

moon and the stars, the hea-vens so grand! Just what is man that you

stay mind-ful of him? Just low-er than an - gels, with glo - ry is crowned!

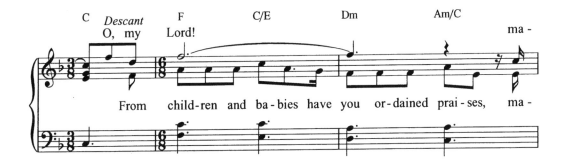

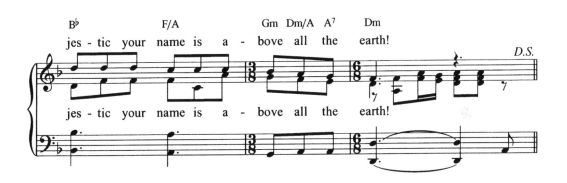

8 Glory to God!
(Gloria in Excelsis Deo!)

Words and Music: Roger Jones arr. Annie Routley
From *Simeon* (1997)

ST GERMAIN Irregular and Refrain

9 God is with us, Emmanuel

Words and Music: Roger Jones
From *Precious and Honoured* (1995)

OVERTON 8 8 10 10 10 7

Gently flowing (♩ = 105)

God is with us, Em-man-u-el!

God is with us, good news to tell.

For now the Sa-viour of the world has come.

He came in-to the world to make his home.

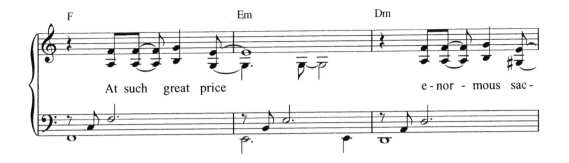

At such great price e - nor - mous sac-

- ri - fice! For now our God is with us!

10 He is here, here with us
(Wonderful Counsellor)

Words: Alison Fuggle
Music: Roger Jones

DEAKIN

With rhythmic strength (♩ = 90)

1. He is here,
2. You are here,

here with us, stretch out your hands to
here with us, your hands stretch out to

greet him; he is here, here with us, a mys-te-ry!
greet us; you are here, here with us, a mys-te-ry!

He is here, here with us, he
You are here, here with us, with

e - ter - nal Fa - ther, Prince of Peace,

he is here. *(last time: improvised worship phrases)*

You are here!

11 High up on a hillside
(High or low, rich or poor)

Words: Alison Fuggle
Music: Roger Jones

FUGGLE

With feeling ($\quarternote$ = 95)

1. High up on a hill-side, shi-ver-ing with cold,
2. In a sta-ble's dark-ness with the smel-ly beasts,
3. Search-ing in the hea-vens, look-ing for a King,

hud-dled in the dark of night;
hud-dled in the dark of night;
hud-dled in the dark of night;

poor, des-pised and hum-ble, first to hear the words:
cra-dl-ing the ba-by born be-fore all time:
trav'l-ling from all na-tions, wel-comed from a-far:

'High and low, come wor-ship in God's light!'

Chorus

High or low, rich or poor, wise or fool-ish, good

12 Hush, hush, don't make a sound

Words: Brenda Nansen
Music: Roger Jones. From *Away in a Manger* (1989)

KEWSTOKE 66 75 and Refrain

Moderato con moto

1. If we gent-ly o-pen the door and take a lit-tle peep,

in the sta-ble there we see Je-sus fast a-sleep. Hush! Hush!

Don't make a sound! Je-sus is a-sleep! Hush! Hush!

To next verse

Don't make a sound! *(Spoken)* Je - sus is a - sleep! *Shhh!*

Last time

Je - sus is a - sleep! Je - sus is a -

sleep! Je - sus is a - sleep! *Shhh!*

2. Snuggled in the soft, warm hay,
   Jesus, he is asleep.
   Mary smiles and rests awhile,
   careful watch she keeps.

3. Hear the donkey shuffle his feet
   and oxen move around.
   Just the rustle of their breath
   is the only sound.

13 Infant holy

Words: traditional Polish, trans. Edith Margaret Gellibrand Reed (1885-1933)
Music: Roger Jones

SUTTON COLDFIELD 87 87 88 77

Gently, with rhythm (♩ = 105)

1. In-fant ho-ly, in-fant low-ly, for his bed a cat- -tle stall; ox-en low-ing, lit-tle know-ing Christ the Babe is Lord of all. Swift are wing-ing

an-gels sing - ing,   no-wells ring - ing,   ti - dings bring - ing,

Christ the Babe   is Lord   of   all,   Christ the Babe   is

Lord   of   all.

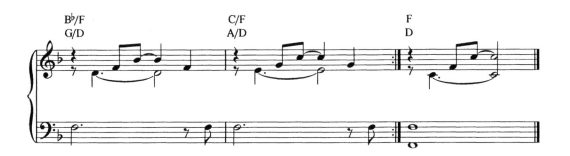

2. Flocks were sleeping, shepherds keeping
   vigil till the morning new;
   saw the glory, heard the story,
   tidings of a gospel true.
   Thus rejoicing, free from sorrow,
   praises voicing, greet tomorrow,
   Christ the Babe was born for you,
   Christ the Babe was born for you!

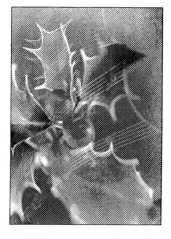

14 In the bleak midwinter

Words: Christina Georgina Rossetti (1830-1894)
Music: Roger Jones arr. Annie Routley. From *While Shepherds Watched* (1987)

BARNT GREEN Irregular

Andante con moto (♩ = 80)

1. In the bleak mid-
3. An - gels and arch-
4. What can I

win - ter fros - ty wind made moan,
an - gels may have ga-thered there,
give him, poor as I am?

earth stood hard as ir - on, wa - ter like a
che - ru - bim and ser-a-phim thronged the
If I were a shep - herd, I would bring a

stone; snow had fal-len, snow on snow,
air; but on - ly his mo - ther
lamb; if I were a wise man

15 I will magnify
(Mary's Magnificat)

Words and Music: Roger Jones arr. Annie Routley
From *While Shepherds Watched (1987)*

CASTLE BROMWICH 10 4 D and Refrain

Andante con moto

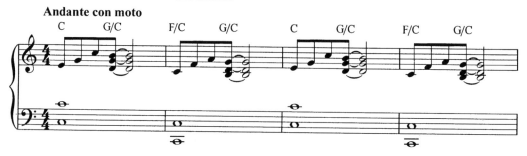

Chorus

I will mag-ni-fy your name, O Lord.

last time rall.

I re-joice for you have saved me,

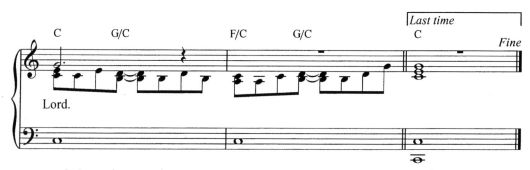

Lord.

Last time
Fine

1. You have been mind-ful of my hum-ble state. I serve you,

Lord. All ge-ne-ra-tions now will call me bless'd

from this day forth!

2. The mighty one has done great things for me,
   holy his name!
   On those who fear him now his mercy rests,
   each age the same.

3. With strength his arm performs such mighty deeds
   scatters the proud.
   He lifts the lowly but the mighty kings,
   he brings them down.

4. He fills the hungry, but the rich he sends
   empty away.
   He keeps the promise made to Abraham
   each day today.

16 Jesus, baby Jesus

Words and Music: Roger Jones. From *Stargazers* (1976)

FINLAY 65 65 D

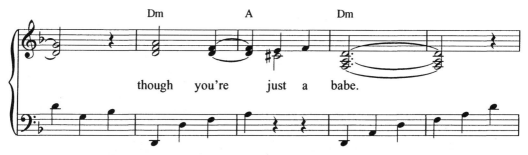

mf Sa - viour, as you're sleep - ing, Sa - viour,

are you mine? Je - sus, though a ba - by,

Je - sus, you're di - vine.

For Mary

17 Love came down at Christmas

Words: Christina Georgina Rossetti (1830-1894)
Music: Roger Jones arr. Annie Routley

STAR AND ANGEL 67 67

Moderato (♩ = 96)

1. Love came down at Christ-mas,
love all love-ly, love di-vine; love was born at Christ-mas,
star and an - gel gave the sign.

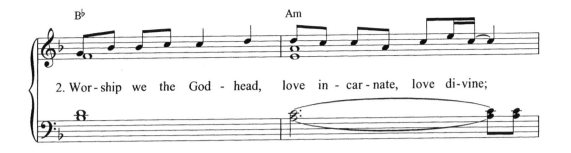

2. Wor - ship we the God - head, love in - car - nate, love di - vine;

wor - ship we our Je - sus: but where-with the sac - red sign?

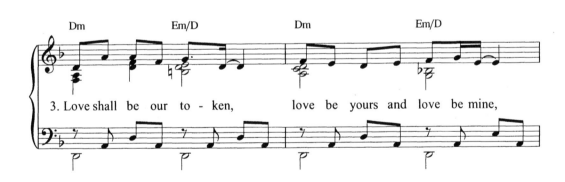

3. Love shall be our to - ken, love be yours and love be mine,

love to God and all men, love for plea and gift and

sign.

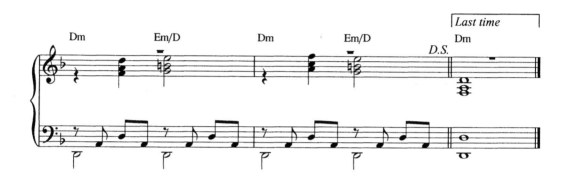

Last time

D.S.

18 Mary and her man called Joe

Words: Martin Parry
Music: Roger Jones arr. Annie Routley. From *Simeon* (1997)

GRENFELL 77 77 D and Refrain

Relaxed (♩ = 95)

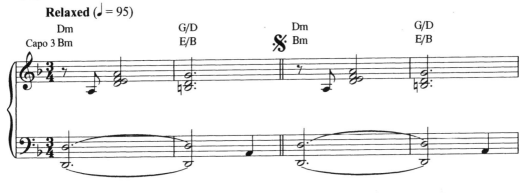

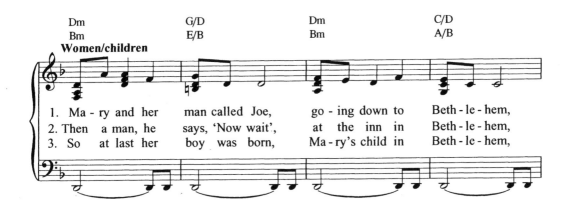

1. Ma - ry and her man called Joe, go - ing down to Beth - le - hem,
2. Then a man, he says, 'Now wait', at the inn in Beth - le - hem,
3. So at last her boy was born, Ma - ry's child in Beth - le - hem,

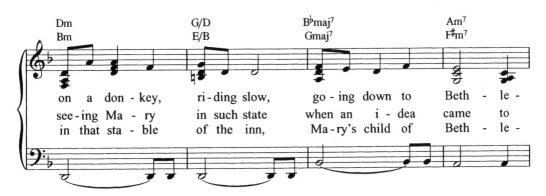

on a don - key, ri - ding slow, go - ing down to Beth - le -
see - ing Ma - ry in such state when an i - dea came to Beth - le -
in that sta - ble of the inn, Ma - ry's child of Beth - le -

Men/Congregation

Ma - ry's ba - by due so soon, Jo - seph asks them
'I've a sta - ble, pret - ty dry, nice and warm, give
In the heav'ns the an - gels sang, hal - le - lu - jahs

Dm   G/D   Dm
Bm   E/B   Bm

hem.
him.
hem.

'Is there room?' 'Sor - ry' they all say to him, 'There
it a try. All I have, not much I fear, but
rang and rang. Peace on earth, good - will to men,

C/D   Dm   G/D
A/B   Bm   E/B

is no room in Beth - le - hem.'
all you're going to find 'round here.'
through the child of Beth - le - hem.

B♭maj⁷   Am⁷   Dm
Gmaj⁷   F♯m⁷   Bm

Go - ing

Men/Congregation

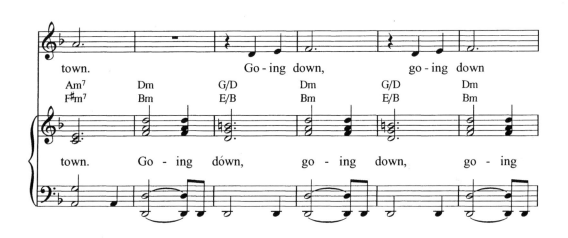

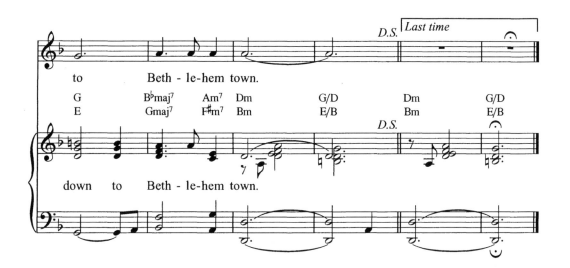

19 O little town of Bethlehem

Words: Phillips Brooks (1835-1893)
Music: Roger Jones arr. Annie Routley. From *Simeon* (1997)

the e-ver-last - ing light;

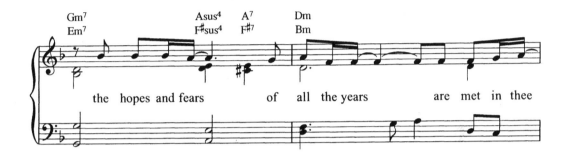

the hopes and fears of all the years are met in thee

to - night.

Optional harmony for verse 3 will be found overleaf

2. O morning stars, together
proclaim the holy birth,
and praises sing to God the King,
and peace to men on earth;
for Christ is born of Mary;
and, gathered all above,
while mortals sleep, the angels keep
their watch of wond'ring love.

3. How silently, how silently
the wondrous gift is giv'n!
So God imparts to human hearts
the blessings of his heav'n.
No ear may hear his coming,
but in this world of sin,
where meek souls will receive him, still
the dear Christ enters in.

4. O holy Child of Bethlehem,
descend to us, we pray;
cast out our sin, and enter in,
be born in us today.
We hear the Christmas angels
the great glad tidings tell:
O come to us, abide with us,
our Lord Emmanuel.

Optional harmony for verse 3

3. How si-lent-ly, how si-lent-ly the won-drous gift is giv'n!

So God im-parts to hu - man hearts the bles-sings of

his heav'n. No ear may hear his com - ing,

but in this world of sin, where meek souls will re -

ceive him, still the dear Christ en - ters in.

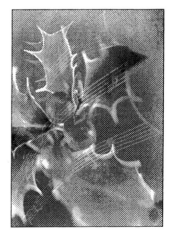

20 Riding high and low

Words and Music: Roger Jones. From *Stargazers* (1976)

ASTON MANOR 55 65 and Refrain

Allegro ma non troppo

1. Ri - ding high and low, look - ing for a king,

ri - ding o - ver des - erts, with the gifts we bring.

Frank - in - cense and myrrh, gold we bring to him,

these are what we'll give, and our hearts to him. him.

2. Over mountains high,
   over deserts dry.
   On to find this baby,
   looking in the sky!

3. On we go to Herod,
   but he'll turn so green
   when we tell of Jesus,
   and the star we've seen.

4. We are nearly there,
   might get there today,
   star is still above us,
   showing us the way.

21 Sheep!

Words and Music: Roger Jones arr. Annie Routley
From *While Shepherds Watched* (1987)

SHEEP Irregular
Allegretto vivace ($\mathbf{\,d} = 64$)

Chorus

Sheep!   Sheep!   Is there a-ny-thing more to   life than sheep?

Last time   *Fine*

Sheep!   Sheep!   Is there a-ny-thing more than   sheep?

To verses

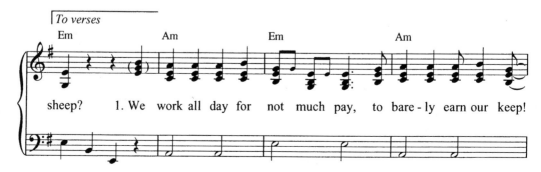

sheep?   1. We work all day for   not much pay, to bare-ly earn our keep!

In bed at night, can you guess our plight?

Spoken: (Yawn)   I can't sleep! *Sung:* We end up count-ing sheep!

2. King David was a shepherd-boy,
   at night he used to keep
   his watchful eye on his flocks, but why?
   (Spoken) Someone please tell me why
   (Sung) should anyone want his sheep!

3. We go to town, but people frown
   as 'round the streets we creep.
   'Not welcome here! Out of town, d'you hear!
   (Spoken) In the fields, that's your place!
   (Sung) Go back to keep your sheep!'

4. Oompah, oompah! There's a woolly jumpah!
   No, it's just a lamb!
   What can it be? Is it plain to see?
   (Spoken) Is it him? Is it her? Is it you or me?
   (Sung) No, it's just a ewe or ram!

22 What was it like for the shepherds?

Words: Mary Wright
Music: Roger Jones arr. Annie Routley. From *Away in a Manger* (1989)

BARTLETT 87 88 and Refrain

2. What was it like for the shepherds
   seeing an angel out there?
   What was it like for the shepherds
   so scared by the sudden bright glare?

3. What was it like for the shepherds
   leaving the sheep in the cold?
   What was it like for the shepherds
   to do as the angel had told?

4. There was great joy for the shepherds
   leaving their fields cold and wild!
   There was great joy for the shepherds
   on seeing the newly-born child.

23 While shepherds watched

Words: Nahum Tate (1652-1715)
Music: Roger Jones arr. Annie Routley. From *While Shepherds Watched* (1987

CLENT HILLS CM

Allegro (♩ = 160)

While shep - herds watched, while shep - herds

watched, while shep - herds watched,

while shep - herds

watched. 1. While shep - herds watched their flocks by night, all

seat - ed on the ground, the an - gel of the

3. To you in David's town this day
   is born of David's line
   a Saviour, who is Christ the Lord;
   and this shall be the sign:

4. The heav'nly Babe you there shall find
   to human view displayed,
   all meanly wrapped in swathing bands,
   and in a manger laid.'

5. Thus spake the seraph, and forthwith
   appeared a shining throng
   of angels praising God, who thus
   addressed their joyful song:

6. 'All glory be to God on high
   and to the earth be peace,
   goodwill henceforth from heav'n to men
   begin and never cease.'

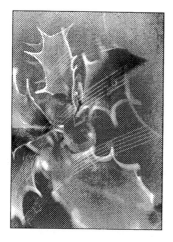

24 Why should I be so favoured?
(Mary's Magnificat)

Words and Music: Roger Jones arr. Annie Routley
From *Simeon* (1997)

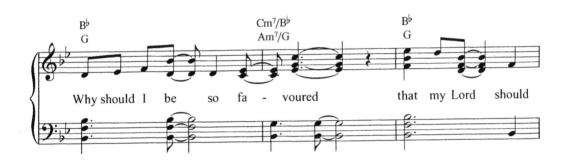

Why should I be so fa - voured that my Lord should

vi - sit me? He has be-come my Sa - viour,

caus - ing me to sing: I will

25 Yeshua, Messiah

Words: Alison Fuggle
Music: Roger Jones arr. Annie Routley. From *Snakes and Ladders* (1997)

YESHUA
Israeli feel (♩ = 120)

Ye - shu - a, Mes - si - ah,

Je - sus, Lamb of God,   A - do - nai,   Im - man-

Last time to Coda

- u - el,   you are God with   us.   Ye - shu-

Other works by Roger Jones

Jerusalem Joy – Easter musical, from Palm Sunday to Easter Day

Stargazers – Christmas musical – the story of the Wise Men

Apostle – Musical of St Paul's conversion (Acts 9)

David – Musical of the Old Testament story of David and Goliath

A Grain of Mustard Seed – Musical about Robert Raikes, founder of Sunday Schools

Saints Alive! – Pentecost musical – the birth of the Church (Acts 1 and 2)

Greater than Gold – Musical about Welsh girl Mary Jones and her Bible

From Pharaoh to Freedom – Musical about the Passover – Old and New Testament

The Chosen Few – Collection of 16 worship songs, including a wedding song

Tell Me the Stories of Jesus – Song book for all ages (cassette also available)

While Shepherds Watched – Christmas musical – the shepherds and the birth of Christ

The Torn Curtain – Musical about Tabernacle worship, including a Communion setting

Away in a Manger – A children's nativity musical

Mary Magdalene – Musical about a woman saved, healed and delivered by Jesus

Ways to Praise – Songbook containing 22 psalms, hymns and songs (also on CD/tape)

Jairus' Daughter – Musical about Jesus the healer

Angel Voices – Musical based upon themes from the book of Revelation

Precious and Honoured – 21 psalms, hymns and songs of worship and healing (also on CD/tape)

Jesus Rode a Donkey – Selection on cassette of favourites from Roger Jones' musicals

Pharisee – Musical about Nicodemus, the Pharisee who came to Jesus at night

Simeon – Nativity musical through the eyes of Simeon (Luke 2)

Snakes and Ladders – Musical spanning the whole Bible – the ups and downs of God's people

Roger Jones Hymn Collection – 41 new settings of well-loved words. Published by Kevin Mayhew. (Also on CD/tape and accompaniment CD/tape.)

Many of the above musicals are available in a music book, words booklet, CD, cassette, accompaniment CD/cassette, Bible studies, drama, instrumental or orchestral parts or demo video. Please contact Christian Music Ministries to place an order:

Christian Music Ministries, 325 Bromford Road, Hodge Hill, Birmingham, B36 8ET
Tel: 0121 783 3291 Fax: 0121 785 0500 Web: www.cmm.org.uk